# Down Shady Lane

# Down Shady Lane

## Revelations of A Botanical Medium

Leslie K Waters

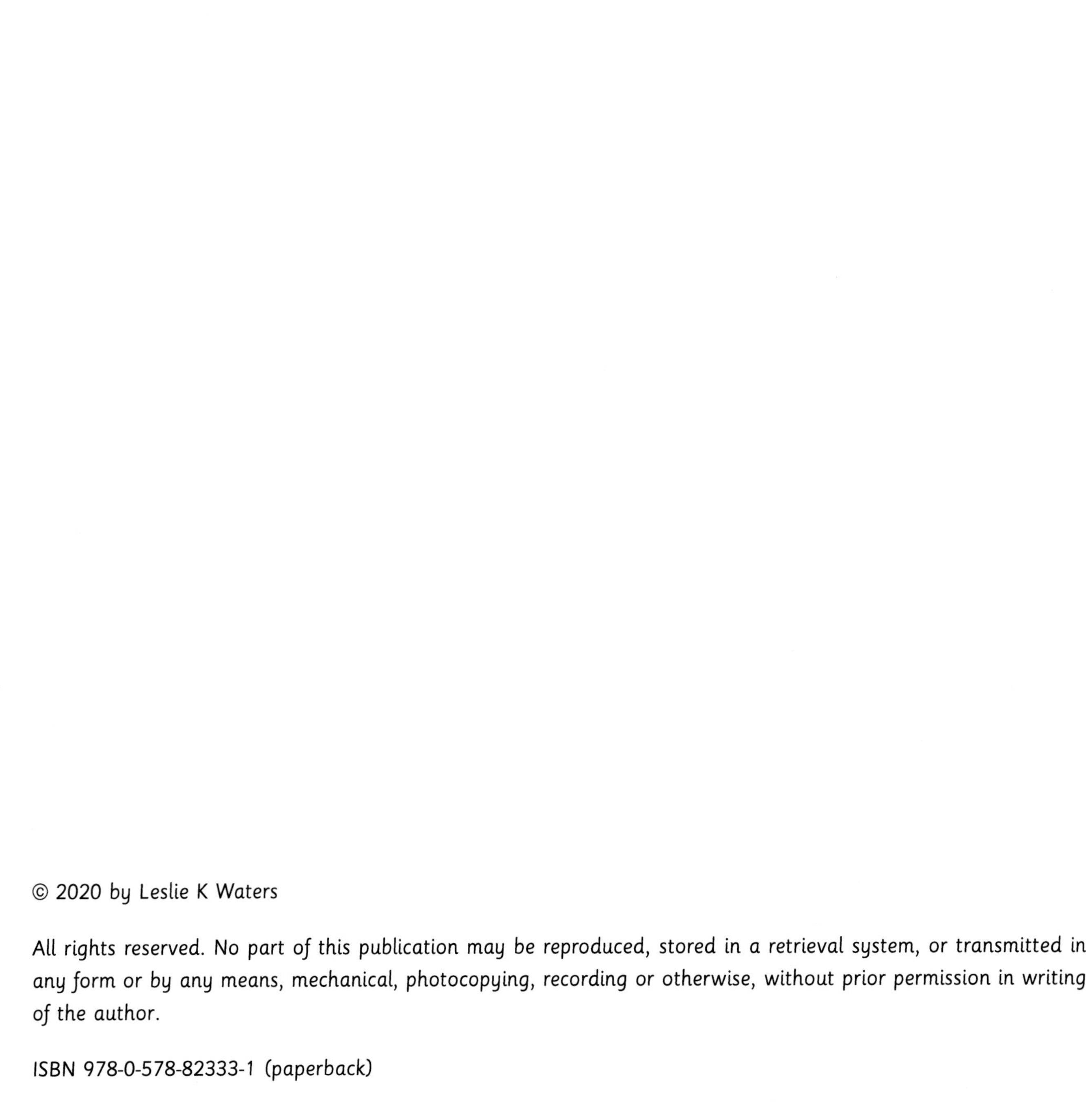



ISBN 978-0-578-82333-1 (paperback)

*This book is dedicated to my parents*
*who instilled in me a fascination*
*with the natural world and*
*to my beloved friends who over the years*
*have provided me with an abundant supply*
*of support, encouragement and laughter*
*through both sunny and cloudy days.*

# Table of Contents


Prologue ix

Chapter 1 Aging Beauties 1
Chapter 2 Environmental Concerns 13
Chapter 3 As The Bark Burns 25
Chapter 4 Growing Pains 37
Chapter 5 Flora Culture 48
Chapter 6 Green Gleanings 61
Chapter 7 Botanical Queries 74
Chapter 8 Perennial Ponderings 87
Chapter 9 Seasons and Holidays 99
Chapter 10 Politics and Miscellany 111

Epilogue 123

# Prologue

It was hot. It was a Saturday afternoon. I was doing lawn work out in the side yard. Maybe it was the fact that I hadn't eaten lunch. Maybe it was the heat. Okay, it's Florida, **maybe** it was the humidity. The next thing I knew, I was down on the ground. My eyes closed, I started to hear all sorts of voices. "What should we do?" "Are adult people supposed to fall down like that?" "See what happens when they don't get enough water?"

When I opened my eyes, I was startled to see there was no one around. Yet still the voices continued. Then I suddenly realized: I was hearing THE PLANTS! Yes, an entire kingdom was communicating and I could hear them! Somehow I had become a botanical medium.

What can I say? I really should have seen this coming. After reviewing various comments people had made about me throughout my life, I now see the pattern toward my destiny as it emerged. Here is a summary of their abbreviated (and cleaned-up) comments:

Parents: The child is out playing in the woods again.

Second Grade Teacher: Look! Your lima bean seed has sprouted before anyone else's. You must have a green thumb! (I looked at both of them; I didn't, but I do have green eyes.)

Garden and Hardware Shop Employee: That kid is constantly loitering around the flower bulb bins and suspiciously eyeing the racks of our vegetable seed packets.

Piano Teacher: Pupil only wants to play songs exalting nature and/or floral life.

Science Teacher: Memorized the equation for photosynthesis as though all life depended on it. (In case you've forgotten – $6CO_2 + 6H_2O = C_6H_{12}O_6 + 6O_2$.)

First Boss: Wastes entirely too much time looking out the windows at the flowers, shrubs and trees on the grounds.

Art Teacher: Ignores art assignments regarding the human form. Focuses all attention on the botanical.

Horticulture Teacher: Would rather sketch plants in notebook than tend them; resists pruning or pinching in the garden.

Additional Twenty Years of Bosses: Regularly dispenses unsolicited prescriptive advice on the care and feeding of office plants. On the other hand, office has never looked greater or greener.

So there you have it. Now you know how it all started and why, I suppose, I had come to be chosen.

As you can imagine, this obviously isn't the sort of thing one goes running to friends and neighbors or even family about, at least not until giving it much thought. But the next day even more voices continued. Soon, I began to hear them all – trees, bushes, grass, fruit, vegetables ... you name it.

"But wait," you ask, "what can all these plants possibly be thinking and talking about?" Hah! They have plenty to share, from the topical to the philosophical, the silly to the sublime, and want me to pass this on. They might even teach you a thing or two. They have me. But be forewarned! It's quite possible your life may never be the same after you take that trip with me *Down Shady Lane*.

# Chapter 1
# Aging Beauties

This was back at the end of the century – the twentieth century that is – and later that fateful day, I thought perhaps I had whacked myself on the head when I fell down and sustained a concussion or traumatic brain injury. A quick self-check and no, my pupils were equally dilated and I wasn't nauseous, full of ear ringing or with headache, so I wasn't about to rack up a hospital bill. I had gone to bed not knowing quite what to expect from the entire incident. Being inside the house was much quieter, except for the occasional peep from the cut flower arrangement on the dining room table and the houseplant mumbling something or other in the den.

At first it was the trees I could hear most clearly, evidently because they're the oldest, largest and loudest – assuming, as I said, that this was indeed what I was hearing.

The trees generally are quite aware that they usually live decades longer than we "walky-talkies," as I've since heard them refer to us humans, and they've had plenty

of experience worrying about aging and its effects. They were very excited to learn that I could "hear" them and then relay their thoughts. But with this privilege comes the responsibility of trying to best depict their sentiments in both artistry and text. I modestly told them I may not be the best person to portray either their thoughts or feelings, but they matter of factly told me, with unanimous underwhelming enthusiasm lest I get a swelled head at this honor, "Eh, you'll do. We'll work with what we've got."

And if you don't like what they have to say, don't shoot me; remember, I'm just the botanical medium who is the messenger.

As I cannot take credit for their comments, thoughts and ideas that are portrayed in the drawings, our partnership is acknowledged with a "Lesleaf" on each one. This is the plant kingdom permitting the drawing's release and blessing it with a seal of approval. Do forgive them if their very forthcoming ideas were sometimes wordy, quite verbose and otherwise downright garrulous. They haven't learned, to quote Shakespeare, that "Brevity is the soul of wit." However, in most cases, it was nice to note their senses of humor are often remarkably similar to mine.

Here is a sample of their aging concerns.

"It's not that I begrudge them the worms,
Maggie, but some mornings,
I'd just like to sleep in."

"I'm awfully sorry, Ma'am, but we've done everything possible. Even if he does come out of the coma, he'll still only be a vegetable."

"You know, Fred, you really oughta try it. A few good sessions with the right massage therapist might just knock some of those kinks and knots right out of you."

"Ah, you young whippersnappers've got it easy. When I was your age I had to hunt for nutrients all over the place. Now they lay tree spikes right at your feet."

"Gosh, Harriet, it's amazing!
That new tree surgeon did wonders for you.
You don't look a day over a hundred!"

Quality
Time
"At our age we've been picked
over and cast aside, but this Cezanne
guy says there's still life left in us."
Les

"Naturally I'm glad we're still together, Cora. I just didn't figure this was where we'd wind up spending our golden years."

"No, Sweetie. Grandpa has no interest in seeing the lower forty converted into a strip mall. He already has everything he needs right here."

"Don't be ridiculous, Winnifred,
at our age a little girth looks good!"

"First, there was the treadmill. Then the recumbent bike and now the rowing machine. John, dear, you've simply got to resist buying all these gadgets you know you're never going to use."

# Chapter 2
# Environmental Concerns

Some indoor plants can get pretty talkative with me. Should I enter a business establishment or restaurant, there are often planter beds that are full of chatter for me to hear. I do try to assist them; however, it is one thing to ask the waiter for a glass of water once you are seated, but quite another to let the hostess know on the way to your table that the plants over by table eight told me they need a good drenching.

Outdoor plants, on the other hand, have their own ideas on the environment and it is a main topic for them. I must say that they tend to have been around a lot longer than we humans, and once the trees realized that I could be made aware of any matters that concerned them, their attention did turn to more serious issues. Maybe we should heed their advice on these subjects.

"I'm afraid there're no mistakes in the calculations. Even if he takes two of each, he'll still only need the canoe."

"Ladies and gentlemen, the secret to success can be summed up in two words: conserve water."

Chainsaw Massacre

"None of this would have happened, you know, if years ago, like us, they'd all gone solar!"

"Obviously being an endangered species has its advantages. It's just too bad you have to reach the brink of extinction to get there."

"K-2, Everest, Denali! They ain't seen nothin' till they've all fallen from Hubbert's peak!"

"First there was the soil erosion and runoff. Now there're mudslides! You know, it's not easy going through life feeling like you're always losing ground!"

# Fruit Pie Charts

"Look. They make us itch, cough, wheeze and sneeze. The figures bear me out. The only thing pesticide have ever done for us as a group is save us from the organic vegetarian."

"Air pollution, soil erosion, acid rain! Whine, whine, whine...it's not like we can just pick up and move, Martha."

"Hey, buddy, I wouldn't knock global warming, climate change, whatever. It's the only environmental disaster where we stand a fighting chance."

In addition, the plants let me know in no uncertain terms that they would appreciate if you would make the attempt to learn their botanical name rather than only their common name – that is to say, their binomial nomenclature. Just as you have a first name and a last name, so do they. It would be best for all if you would learn theirs. They know yours! (Sometimes from your mailbox.) Besides, it will help when you go to the store to purchase their fertilizer or learn their sun, shade and watering requirements in your yard. You will find some of these genera and species sprinkled liberally throughout this little volume. The two-part genus and species format in Latin is more like stating a last and then a first name, like they do in Japan or Hungary. And if they have a cultivar, which is like a nickname, it is given in 'single quotes' right after their first name.

And while you're at it, when you buy a new plant, give it a pet name that reflects its genus and species. For example, if you purchase a new river birch tree (*Betula nigra)*, you could call it Betty. That will help you in recalling its Latin name down the road. (Please be sure that the selection process is made in cooperation with all family members because the plant needs to feel wanted by all parties. It would hate to see you in need of sessions with a horticultural counselor.)

## Chapter 3

# As The Bark Burns

Plants often have trouble getting a relationship started. Trees, unlike your annuals, might bide their time for years, until they are mature. Some of them seem particularly resentful that they don't have their own version of a sexy magazine to tide them over in the interim. They have suggested to me that I would be fulfilling a tree-mendous need if I could convince a publisher to give them a periodical of their own since they can't do it themselves. Already their suggestions for section features have included:

1) How to Spot Virgin Timber
2) Seed Dispersal: Going Further, Faster and Longer
3) Beating the Blight Blues
4) Fungal Follies – How to Recognize and Avoid Them
5) Curing Flaky Bark

Once they are ready to commit, they'll send out trial balloons, *feelers for* pollen possibilities. And when the relationship is established there are the usual yet unpredictable ups and downs *of* evaporation and precipitation like those *of* the hydrological cycle.

So you know they are going to have their sentiments, *feelings* and petty jealousies in their relationships with each other.

"Psst...have you heard? Laura uses leaf gloss. Pass it on!"

"Harvey, I really don't care how salt-tolerant we mangroves are as a species. Don't you think five tequilas are enough?"

Herman tried his best to fit in with the other birds of paradise till he realized it was not possible. He wasn't simply a bigger bird; he was a Giant Bird of Paradise.

"I don't care if you are descended from a long line of purebred impatiens, Reginald, that's still no excuse to get testy with me!"

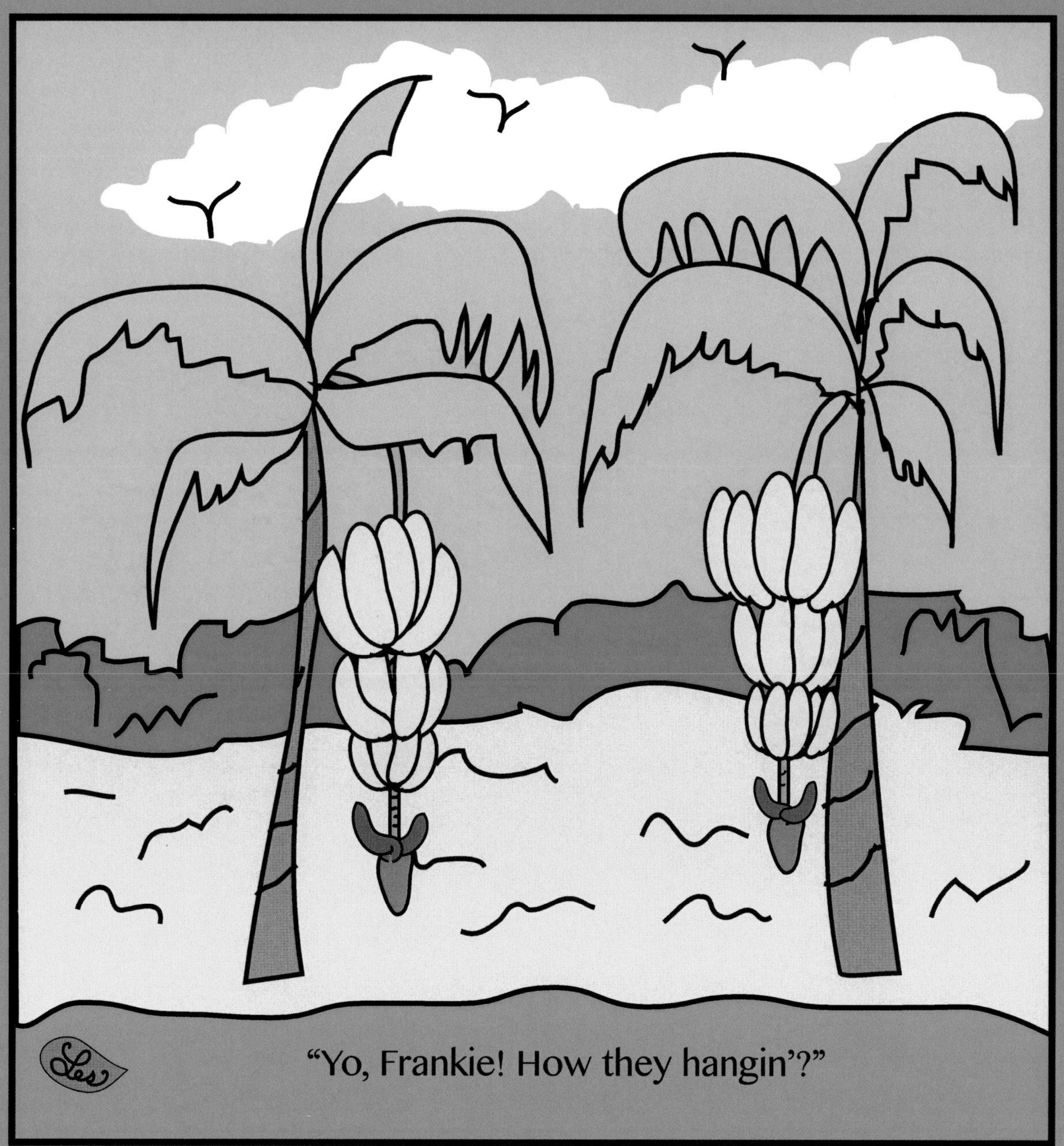


"Yo, Frankie! How they hangin'?"

"Oh, Persival, I may pollinate with others from time to time when the winds of chance blow my way, but you'll always have my heartwood."

"Of course everything's coming up roses!
What? You were expecting, maybe,
chrysanthemums?"

Conventionally
Speaking
"Bart, you CAN'T come down with a cold just
before the Fifth National Echinacea Convention!
You wanna give the rest of us a bad rep?"
Les

"Psst! Picked up any good pollen lately?"

"And for heaven's sake, Margot, this time let's not invite the Kava Kava sisters or the Valerians. I've nothing against them personally, but they seem to put all our guests to sleep!"

# Chapter 4
# Growing Pains

The trees, being perennials, have a chance to watch their offspring grow up. They have distinct ideas and advice on raising and nurturing their young. Just the same as we walky-talky parents, some of them are strict and old-fashioned in their ideas while others are more fun-filled and encouraging. Either way, they are usually very proud of their progeny.

The older trees will lay down the law to the younger about the value of a dollar, because after all money doesn't, well, grow on them. I have heard this goes down fine with all but the silver dollar eucalyptus (*Eucalyptus cinerea*) who take umbrage at this statement. The Tree of Gold (*Tabebuia aurea*) also express a bit of opposition but not quite as strongly. As long as we follow the money and acknowledge their unique monetary names they are okay with this.

"We cling peaches have always stuck together, Archibald. I'm not sure we should let any of our offspring bum around with some freestone."

"I'm pleased as punch, Rita, that she can recite Avogadro's number, but she won't grow anywhere in life till she's learned to photosynthesize."

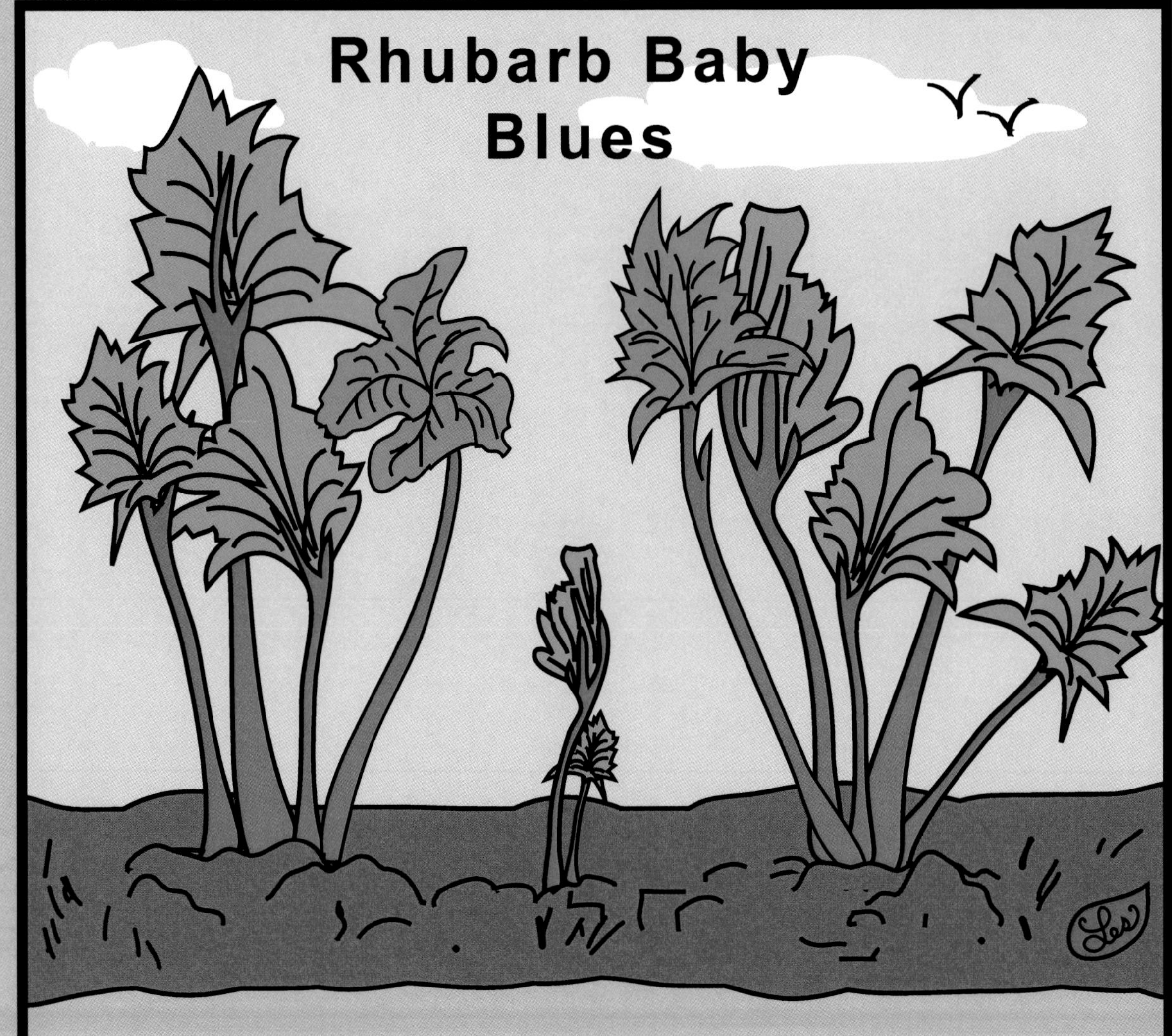


"He's bound to be depressed, dear. He's going through that awkward phase – deciding if he'd rather associate with the fruits or with the vegetables."

"Isn't it wonderful, dear? Our littlest papaya has turned out to be monoecious!"

"We'll not hear anymore of this nonsense about cloning, John-Boy. On this mountain we do things like that the old-fashioned way."

"Aw, c'mon, Dad. Tell us the one about George Washington again. Puhleeease!!!"

"Just have him take two tablespoons of minor elements tonight and call me... in a few days to a few weeks."

"Here in this nursery, boys, you best grow up fast and mean. You might say it's a dogwood eat dogwood world."

"And boy, no matter how far you grow in life, never, ever, neglect your roots."

"Stand tall and be proud, son, you're from Idaho. Compared to us, all the others are just small potatoes!"

## Chapter 5

# Flora Culture

Was it only the plants in *my* yard that I heard? Oh, not at all. Over the years, when I went to friends' homes, I heard the voices there also. I have to be mindful that not all of my friends are willing to accept my special capability. For example, to help the trees it is one thing to say that my years of horticultural training have enabled me to note that their Phoenix palm tree is turning yellow and needs magnesium, but hard for some of them to accept my saying, "On my way to your front door, your gardenias asked me to let you know you are about six weeks overdue in putting out their chelated iron." I hope you notice the distinction between these two approaches.

It is delightful to have learned that most of the plants are quite attuned to all the arts and aspects of our culture of television, music, movies and fairy tales. There was one time I overheard a couple of forest pines conversing about an old story:

Pine 1: Have you heard the latest scuttlebutt on Goldilocks?
Pine 2: No, what?

Pine 1: They finally threw the book at her! She's down at Juvy.

Pine 2: It's about time! Maybe now the three bears and the rest of this forest can get some peace.

I like to think they were joking, more or less putting me on, so I would think that they can't tell truth from fiction. Over the years, I've come to the conclusion that some can, while others cannot.

"Lately, Ward, I've been rather concerned about the beaver."

"I heard you really made quite an impression on that Monet fellow."

"Pruning? PRUNING?!
We don't need no stinkin' pruning!"

"Yup. It was definitely slick advertising got us here, Margie. Sure, we've noticed a few buffalo roaming, but we've never seen the deer or the antelope play."

Fairy Tale
Impressions
Les
“That Bambi! What a ham! Always performing for an audience. Oh, and don’t even get me started on Snow White and all seven of those dwarfs.”

"I don't care if we are traditional symbols of hospitality. Some days I just don't feel like company."

"To bloom or not to bloom? Please! Spare us the theatrics, Hamlet. Are you going to waste the whole summer again on that debate?"

"Yes, you'll find life here on the farm is really quite peaceful. Oh, there's the occassional quack-quack here and oink-oink there. A moo-moo here or cluck-cluck there. But eventually you won't even hear the old man's E-I-E-I-O."

"Ahh... Van Gogh. There was an artist who could capture our true essence, eh, Jean-Pierre?"

"I still say they got you on a bum rap, Eddie. They shoulda tested that bough before they go puttin' cradles and babies up there."

Special note: The lawns I've heard have mentioned that their favorite TV show was *Green Acres* and their favorite movie was (what else?) *Splendor in the Grass*. But their favorite line was from the movie where they thought the great Greta Garbo said something to the effect that "I want to be a lawn." I tried to explain that she said "alone" not "a lawn" but the subtleties of a Swedish accent are far too complex for them. The blades became annoyed with me, so I chose not to destroy their illusion. After all, they don't have much of a chance to develop physically, let alone intellectually, with their weekly mowing, and this belief apparently has given them some sort of happiness. I ask, what right do I have to take it from them?

And when the grass sees that it is greener on the other side, the blades might take notice that there were no malfunctioning sprinklers over there. But basically they're a pretty happy, rather Zen-like, contented lot, living in the present. This suits them best. And why not? They haven't much of a future.

# Chapter 6
# Green Gleanings

Well, word began to spread like wildfire (Oops, poor choice of words around plant life – sorry guys!) as to what I was able to do for the plant kingdom* and its various species. My ears were soon overcome by the din of their voices. But one by one, I tried my best to capture their hopes and dreams as well as fears and anxieties.

*Do note, many species are offended by the non-inclusivity of the term "seemingly not mentioning" and its apparent failure to reflect any "queendom" to reflect those of the gentler persuasion, such as lady's slippers (*Cypripedium reginae*), the mother-in-law's tongue (*Dracaena trifasciata*), the woman's tongue tree (*Albizia lebbeck*), Queen Anne's lace (*Daucus carota*), queen sago (*Cycas circinalis*), princess flower bush (*Tibouchina urvilleana*) and the empress or princess Tree (*Paulownia tomentosa*). Oh yes, and those species that are of a dioecious nature – you know, where the male and female are on two separate trees, like your holly (*Ilex opaca*) or cedar (*Juniperus virginiana*). And also papaya (*Carica papaya*) insist on it being

recognized that they can be male, female or hermaphroditic, even changing their choice over their lifetime. I agreed with them that such fluidity does deserve special recognition be they he, she or they!

And plants do have their dreams, albeit sometimes impossible ones. I remember well the time I overheard some tiny young shrubs commenting about their experience with what I assumed to be the weather. One of the plants, little Timothy, and some of his friends said they had already experienced in their brief lives every combination of sporadic drizzles, intermittent downpours and afternoon showers. But someday, just once, they all agreed, it would be wonderful to know what it felt like to take a long hot bath.

In addition, some fruits wonder why they are given different identities depending on their degree of desiccation. For example, dried plums are called prunes and dried grapes become raisins, while apricots stay apricots and dates remain dates. If you have an answer for them, will you be kind enough to let me know? I'll be sure to pass it along.

Lastly, I've known many a flower, fruit or vegetable to wax philosophical, especially the potatoes. They know they are special because they have eyes, but just like a philosopher they ask, "Can any of us say that we really see?" At which time the corn chipped in, "We have ears but do any of us tell you we can really hear?"

"Let's face it, Harry, we're legumes. Even if we can fix our own nitrogen, it's going to be pretty hard for us ever to amount to more than a hill of beans."

"It's great to have a goal, dear,
but how can you be sure that in the loaf of
life, we'll wind up in the upper crust?"

Petal Envy
We Deliver
Betty's Floral Boutique
"Let's face it, fellas. You know we ferns will always be just filler for the flowers."
Les

"I'm warning you, Margaret, don't encourage him with more of your pollen. That one has a strong tendency to drone on and on."

"Sure I'm depressed. I just found out I'm slated to be sliced for a pie. Don't ask me why, but I always had my heart set on being part of a pan dowdy."

"I'm warning you, Esther, don't waste the time you've got left with a bunch of green beans. They'll only string you along."

"I'm delighted you're so optimistic about our possibilities, Alyson, but I believe you are missing the big picture. Roasted, salted, crunchy or creamy, chances are we still wind up in a jar."

## Tater Contemplators

"Granted we all have eyes, but can any of us say we ever really see?"

"Bloom where you're planted? Great! Another new age philosopher who merely restates the obvious."

# Fatalistic Fungi

"We <u>should</u> be nervous about the upcoming corporate merger, Harry. It's ALWAYS the little guys like us that are kept in the dark and then canned."

Yes, the plants know that they can't be like your pets and wag their tails or purr, but they show appreciation for your efforts and kindness with abundant fruit, flowers or a bevy of glossy foliage. This must be an acceptable form of gratitude across phyla.

## Chapter 7

# Botanical Queries

Members of the plant kingdom have their own concerns, petty annoyances and squabbles and they also have their own version of family feuds. I distinctly remember one summer when three members of the Brassica family, the broccoli, broccoflower and cauliflower, were viciously arguing amongst themselves which of them provided the most benefits and therefore had the most value to human beings. Even the cabbage and kale decided to weigh in with their opinions. The rutabaga and the turnips knew better and stayed out of the fray. It became known in their circle as "The Great Cauliflower Kerfuffle." It continues to surface from time to time till this day. Hey, if even the nutritionists can't agree which confers the most benefit in terms of the Indole-3-Carbinol, why should the plants be able to decisively determine it? They don't have access to any testing labs, you know.

And the citrus are a particularly thorny bunch (who argue about which one has the most vitamin C and fiber) – you know, the oranges, tangerines, tangelos, limes and some of the kumquats. It was easy for me to see the rivalries that went on in that family. The magnificent pummelo looking down their branches at all the grapefruit (except for the 'Ruby Reds,' who, as a cultivar with all the hype, think they're pretty hot stuff), the limes and especially lemons. Everyone in that family looked down on the sour lowly lemons. Even their favorite joke reflected their disdain.

> Knock knock.
> Who's there?
> Orange.
> Orange who?
> Orange you glad you're not a lemon.

Also, the cucurbits are a strange lot. There are watermelon wars between the seeded and the seedless varieties in which they debate the merits of their flavor.

And the turnip/rutabaga controversy has more malice then any I've ever seen, even if they know they are not popular anyway. Finally, the yam vs. sweet potato conflict was so involved that it had to be taken to the highest Food Court.

Just like people, plants can sit on a mountain but not on a tack. When they do want to get sage guidance, they've been known to consult a wise old apple tree they affectionately call Dear Crabby. Here is a sample of her no-nonsense approach and straightforward advice:

Dear Crabby: My wife and I have only been together a few months and already she is pollinating with every Tom, Dick and Harry in a ten-mile radius. What should I do? – Disconcerted Tree

Dear Disconcerted: You and your wife are trees and this sort of thing just happens naturally. Obviously you can't move on, so get over it!

While sometimes they try to figure us out.

"Yeah, it's strange but they need cones and signs to remind them to slow down to avoid crushing their young."

"I just don't get it. No matter short, tall, fat, skinny, light, dark, man or woman, they always bring us the same old song and dance about a water shortage."

"I'm tellin' ya it doesn't matter that we're so versatile. We can get diced, sliced, fried, mashed, scalloped, baked, puffed or pureed...nobody cares. We'll always play second fiddle to the meat."

"Yep, that anti-tobacco sentiment runs deep both ways. Not a single one of us said that smoking would be good for them either."

The Right Stuff
USA
"Oh sure, they can send a man to the
moon alright, but can any one of
their kind make oxygen?"
Les

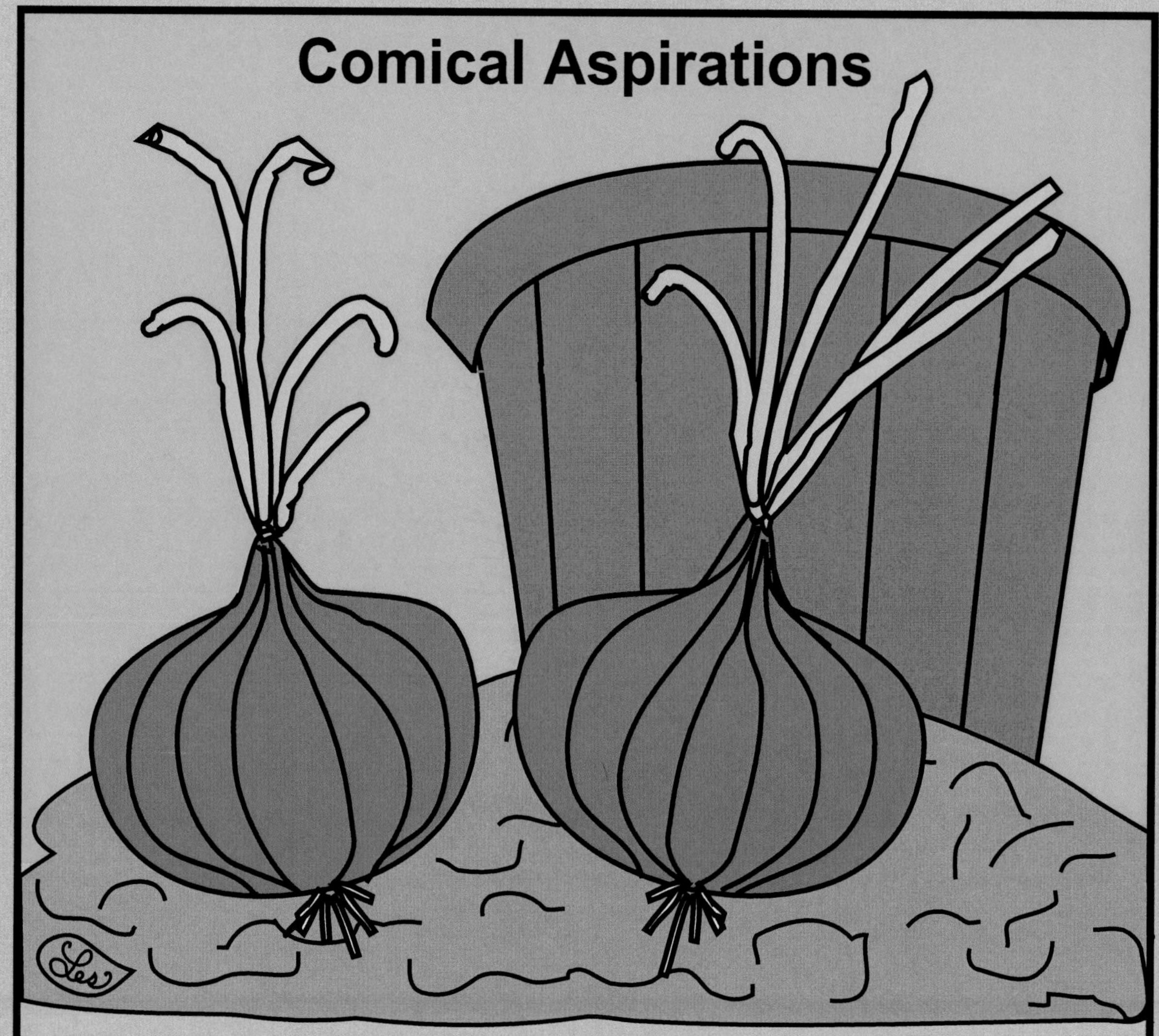


"It's not that they say I stink that depresses me. It's that just once, for a change, I'd like to be able to say I made someone laugh."

"You should have seen it! Mary had a little lamb alright, followed by three helpings of mashed potatoes, a huge bowl of cranberry dressing and an extra generous portion of mincemeat pie. Man, that kid can eat!"

"There's no use pining for the old days, Harriet. Once they've finished screening in our patio, we'll be in a no fly zone."

## Down Shady Lane

"Smart phones! Satellites! 5G! Rockets! With all this high-tech communicating you'd think they could do a better job running this planet."

"Oh for heaven's sake, Marian, look! Here come those botanists again. They're always piddling with our pistils!"

## Chapter 8

# Perennial Ponderings

Unlike annuals, the trees and other perennials have a much better chance at a long life and are able to make many insightful observations. As species, some of the cycads and ginkgo have been around for millennia, but individually, the bristle cone pine is longer lived.

They do not mind my "hearing" their exchanges and are not hesitant to share these views with me. Thus I share them with you.

"Those big red seeds seem to bob around forever.
When will they learn that to put out roots
you've got to settle down?"

Though she tried to feign indifference and a free and independent spirit, deep down Ivy knew she'd always be a clinging vine.

"I don't know about you but the first one or two tattoos seemed tasteful. After that they just made me feel sort of tacky."

"It comes with the territory, Darla.
In this part of the country, you've got to
learn how to live on the ledge."

"That blasted parrot – always looking out for #1. Not once have I ever heard, Polly wants you to water the geraniums."

"Well, there goes the neighborhood!"

Although Eve had diligently gone to therapy for years, she never understood why she continued to hear three voices.

Geographical
Concerns
"Yes, my dearest Dennis! I know we're both
Lily of the Valley! But which valley?
Where the hell are we?"
Les

"Root rot? You think you've got root rot? I'll show you root rot!"

Oh yes. They also have a few concerns that are of a rather delicate interspecies nature.

"Uh-oh, Betty, watch out! Here comes that near-sighted, love-sick poodle again..."

## Chapter 9

# Seasons and Holidays

What of the seasons and the holidays? Plants and humans are going to have an entirely different perspective on them, aren't they? Well, yes and no. It often depends on how they are affected.

The trees know that if they were around before you were born and there are no records of it, you certainly don't know *their* birthday. They forgive you for not celebrating their special day; besides, they get recognized on Arbor Day, which in case you've forgotten, is the last Friday in April. On the other hand, the shrubs and plants have told me that if you got them at a local nursery, you could use as their birthdays the day you adopted them and took them home. This would suit them immensely. A chorus of "Happy Birthday" would be much appreciated, along with an extra helping of a needed dose of fertilizer.

And before you go to dig the hole where they will be planted, do yourself a favor and take a file to sharpen your shovel. For safety reasons, the shovels don't come from the store that way and over the years they lose their edge.

"Oh, I suppose my fun-lovin' Charlie will want to celebrate New Year's Eve the way we do every year...crack up a little bark and break open a few buds."

Same Old,
Same Old
"It's springtime, Marvin, what do you expect?
Of course we're having boiled eggs
and bird's nest soup, again."
Les

Every year Connie insisted on dropping her buds and blooms during the last week of August. After all, she was from the old school. One simply didn't wear white after Labor Day.

"Life is full of choices, alright! This fall we can either get scooped out for a pie or have a face carved up by some grubby little kid."

"Psst! Look! Marsha's always got
to be the first to show off
the new fall colors."

Famous Last Words
"Whoa! Have you heard who's up for the main course this Thursday? I sure am glad I'm no turkey!"

But let's *face* it, the supposed season of brotherly love is often the hardest for many trees.

"I'm telling you every Christmas it'll be the same thing. First, the partridge shows up followed by the two turtle doves. Next it's the three French hens and those darn calling birds. What am I running here a holiday bed and breakfast?"

"I'll admit it. I have been looking forward to the glitz and glamour of the holidays, but it's still hard to be cut off from my friends and family."

"Every Christmas it's the same old speech, 'Peace on Earth, good will toward men,' and then they chop millions of us down."

Christmas Tree Tips
"Listen, trust me on this. Come December, when they start swinging axes and singing 'O Tannenbaum,' scrunch down and try to look really scrawny."

## Chapter 10

# Politics and Miscellany

Species of the plant kingdom have been around millions of years longer than those of the animal kingdom, but especially longer than we more recent *Homo sapiens*. Their kingdom has had a chance to discover a wonderful world of existence that thrives on diversity. Monoculture is not the norm. Nature will see to it that many niches are filled with a web of life that is interdependent. Well, maybe except for Kudzu (*Pueraria montana*) and Australian pine (*Casuarina equisetifolia*). They seem to prefer to hang with their own kind and suck up all the resources to the exclusion of others, causing serious issues for the rest of the plants in the neighborhood. (Then we also have other plants whose common names are scary enough such as the Strangler Fig, Scorpion Tail, Poison Ivy, Dracula Orchid, Witch Hazel, Devil's Claw, Corpse Flower or Venus Fly Trap. I'll leave you to ponder their preferences at your leisure.) And though they bicker over soil nutrients, sunny airspace and water resources in a slow-motion-violence sort of way, mostly they are shining examples of trying to get along – without guns or bloodshed – no Customs, no borders and no walls.

Naturally they want to weigh in with plenty of comments on personal, political or legal issues.

And We
Can't Vote,
Either
“The reason we’ll never have any political clout?
Isn’t it obvious? We’re all bark and no bite!”

"Don't be ridiculous, Tiffany, we're the ideal participants for an HMO! Even if we live and pay premiums for hundreds of years, we'll never avail ourselves of their services."

Tree Grafitti
CUT THE COMPOST
NUTZ TO YOU
XYLEM SUCKS
OUT YOUR SPROUT
EAT DIRT
YOUR SISTERS GOT BORERS

"Well, let me ask you this. If the status of a territory is so great, how come the other fifty states aren't standing in line to sign up?"

"All right, then. It's been moved and seconded that henceforth we Pygmy Dates refer to ourselves as photosynthetically challenged. All those in favor signify by swaying to, those opposed sway fro."

"I don't know about you, Marion, but I like a guy who leans a little left of center."

"Call me old-fashioned if you will, Cindy, but the only thing I want to hear of tweets and twitters is from the birds in our branches!"

"No, JB, we needn't concern ourselves with the ups and downs of the stock market. All our assets are invested in the land."

"For all their moanin' and groanin', do you know how many of 'em won't even show today?"

Just Say No
to GMO
Leave our
genes alone!
Veggies Unite!
Don't let
them
get
your seeds!
Save our
flavors!
Les

# Epilogue

Well, that's my story and I'm stickin' to it. All along the plants insisted that I do my best to help them relay their thoughts.

But you should get out there and listen. Or listen inside if you choose. A few times I've even thought that were I to take a vacation on a sun-drenched island where I could go snorkeling (should I have learned to listen underwater and should my reputation have preceded me), I might hear a cacophony of kelp beds and sea grass calling.

You see what I can do. Why not check whether you can hear the plant kingdom, too? Okay, maybe you can't really hear them talk, but you can get in tune with them. Many are waiting to share themselves with you, and you could assist me. Trust me, they are there for you, heartwood and soul. Most of them anyway. I know that they would enjoy hearing you laugh and, besides, it sounds better to them than the reverberations from a chainsaw, weed whacker or mower.

Lastly, be advised, if you are very lucky in life and once or maybe twice the universe affords you a special gift that you feel is too good to be true, don't run from it. Accept it, nurture and cherish it and use it in a way that benefits you and others, as I hope I have done for you with mine.

Made in the USA
Columbia, SC
11 February 2021